THOMAS MCKNIGHT

BOOK OF DAYS AND NIGHTS

A BULFINCH PRESS BOOK
LITTLE, BROWN AND COMPANY
BOSTON • TORONTO • LONDON

ISBN 0-8212-2021-7
Designed by Marquand Books, Inc.,
with assistance from Renate McKnight.

Bulfinch Press is an imprint and trademark of
Little, Brown and Company (Inc.)
Published simultaneously in Canada by
Little, Brown & Company (Canada) Limited

PRINTED IN HONG KONG

TROPICAL PARADISE

1

2

3

4

5

6

J A N U A R Y

WINDOW ON CENTRAL PARK

TREE SPIRIT

	7
	8
	9
	10
	11
	12

JANUARY

13

14

15

16

17

18

J A N U A R Y

MADISON SQUARE

A P O L L O   O N   D E L O S

19

20

21

22

23

24

J A N U A R Y

25
26
27
28
29
30
31

JANUARY

R I V I E R A   B R E A K F A S T

EGYPT

	1
	2
	3
	4
	5
	6

FEBRUARY

7

8

9

10

11

12

FEBRUARY

CARNIVAL IN VENICE

PALM BEACH BREAKERS

13

14

15

16

17

18

FEBRUARY

19

20

21

22

23

24

FEBRUARY

TRELLIS GOD

GUADELOUPE

25

26

27

28

29

F E B R U A R Y

1

2

3

4

5

6

MARCH

LA SAMANNA

EGYPTIAN GODDESS

7

8

9

10

11

12

MARCH

13

14

15

16

17

18

MARCH

GRENADA

NICE

19

20

21

22

23

24

M A R C H

25

26

27

28

29

30

31

M A R C H

VILLA ROSA

CLIMBING NUBIAN

	1
	2
	3
	4
	5
	6

APRIL

7

8

9

10

11

12

APRIL

SALISBURY

FESTIVAL OF LIGHT

13

14

15

16

17

18

A P R I L

19

20

21

22

23

24

APRIL

BOSTON   PUBLIC   GARDENS

COSTA MESA

	25
	26
	27
	28
	29
	30

A P R I L

1

2

3

4

5

6

MAY

CANNES

FLORIDA LOGGIA

	7
	8
	9
	10
	11
	12

MAY

13

14

15

16

17

18

M A Y

ITALIAN RIVIERA PATH

CAP FERRAT

19

20

21

22

23

24

M A Y

25
26
27
28
29
30
31

M A Y

S A L Z B U R G

CAP MARTIN

1

2

3

4

5

6

J U N E

7
8
9
10
11
12

JUNE

RAVELLO VILLA RUFOLO

AEGEAN GARDEN

13

14

15

16

17

18

J U N E

19	
20	
21	
22	
23	
24	

J U N E

KOBE OVAL ROOM

P E A C O C K   P O I N T

25

26

27

28

29

30

J U N E

1

2

3

4

5

6

JULY

CAPE ANN

NUBIAN WADING

7

8

9

10

11

12

J U L Y

13

14

15

16

17

18

JULY

MURRAY HILL

AUSTRIAN TOWN

19

20

21

22

23

24

J U L Y

25
26
27
28
29
30
31

J U L Y

GREEN STUDIO

SWANSEA

1

2

3

4

5

6

AUGUST

7	
8	
9	
10	
11	
12	

AUGUST

PORTOFINO

MALIBU

13

14

15

16

17

18

AUGUST

19

20

21

22

23

24

AUGUST

GROVE OF APOLLO

LINO

	25
	26
	27
	28
	29
	30
	31

AUGUST

1

2

3

4

5

6

SEPTEMBER

MIDTOWN PENTHOUSE

MANAROLA

	7
	8
	9
	10
	11
	12

SEPTEMBER

13

14

15

16

17

18

SEPTEMBER

PORT OF CALL II

CASTLE ON THE DANUBE

19

20

21

22

23

24

SEPTEMBER

25

26

27

28

29

30

SEPTEMBER

CASTLE COMBE

CAPTAIN'S JACKET

1

2

3

4

5

6

OCTOBER

7

8

9

10

11

12

OCTOBER

NUBIAN LEAPING THROUGH DAY

HARVEST IN SICILY

_13_

_14_

_15_

_16_

_17_

_18_

OCTOBER

19

20

21

22

23

24

OCTOBER

STOCKBRIDGE

HALLOWEEN

25
26
27
28
29
30
31

O C T O B E R

1

2

3

4

5

6

NOVEMBER

WAINSCOTT

BERESFORD

	7
	8
	9
	10
	11
	12

NOVEMBER

13

14

15

16

17

18

N O V E M B E R

RIDDLE OF THE EGG

TRIUMPH OF SATURN

19

20

21

22

23

24

NOVEMBER

| 25 |
| 26 |
| 27 |
| 28 |
| 29 |
| 30 |

NOVEMBER

S T .   T R O P E Z

AEGEAN NYMPH

1

2

3

4

5

6

DECEMBER

7

8

9

10

11

12

DECEMBER

AUSTRIAN CHRISTMAS

COTSWOLD INN

13

14

15

16

17

18

DECEMBER

19

20

21

22

23

24

DECEMBER

CHRISTMAS EVE

CHRISTMAS IN CONNECTICUT

	25
	26
	27
	28
	29
	30
	31

DECEMBER